Farmer Dan's Ducks

by Natalia De La Rosa
illustrated by Erik Brooks

Farmer Dan looked
for his two ducks.
He looked and looked.
But he did not see them.

Farmer Dan saw the cows.
"Have you seen my ducks?"
said Farmer Dan.

"No," said the cows.

Farmer Dan saw his hens.
He said, "Have you seen
my two ducks?"

"No," said the hens.

Farmer Dan saw his horses. He said, "Have you seen my ducks?"

The horses said, "No."

Farmer Dan saw his pigs.
"Have you seen
my two ducks?"
he said.

"No," the pigs said.

Farmer Dan saw the sheep.
He said, "Have you seen
my ducks?"

"Yes," said the sheep.

13

"Look in the grass,"
said the sheep.

Farmer Dan looked
in the grass.

He did not see
two ducks.

He saw ducks and ducks
and ducks!